Lions

WILLIAM K. DURR • JEAN M. LE PERE • MARY LOU ALSIN

CONSULTANT • **PAUL McKEE**

LINGUISTIC ADVISOR • **JACK E. KITTELL**

HOUGHTON MIFFLIN COMPANY • BOSTON

NEW YORK • ATLANTA • GENEVA, ILLINOIS • DALLAS • PALO ALTO

Illustrated by **TRINA SCHART HYMAN**

Bob

Jim

Sally

Jan

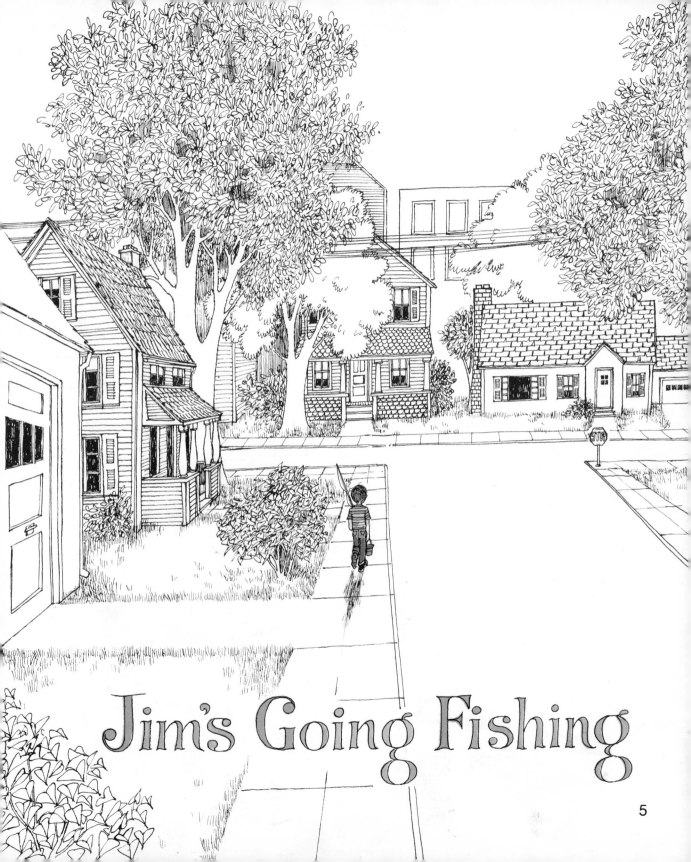

Jim's Going Fishing

Here comes the school bus!
Come on, Jim!

I am not going to school.

You have to go.

I'm going fishing.
And I can't fish in school.

6

Where is Jim?

Jim isn't going to school, Mr. Wills.

Is he sick?

Jim isn't sick.

He wants to go fishing.

7

Jim! Get on the bus!
You have to go to school.

I want to go fishing.
And I can't fish in school.

This is a school day, Jim.

I'm not going today, Mr. Wills.
I have to go fishing.

Jim, where are you going?
This is a school day.

I'm not going to school today.
I want to play.
I'm going to fish here in the park.

9

Fishing on School Days

You can't fish here on school days.
You'll have to go home, Jim.

I can't go home.
And I can't go to school.
I take the bus to school.

10

Where will you go, Jim?

I'll have fun playing in the park.
Fishing and playing are fun.
School isn't fun.

11

This is no fun.

I can't play with Bob.

He's in school.

And I can't play with Mike.

He's in school with Bob.

Is it fun to play in the park, Jim?

No. It's not fun.

I can't go fishing.

And I can't play with Bob and Mike.

I want to go to school.

Can you take me there?

Bob! Mike! Here I am.

I can't go fishing on school days.

You can go fishing there, Jim.

This is a funny day.

I can't fish in the park.

And I can fish in school.

14

1. There is a rocket on TV.

   It is going to the **moon.**

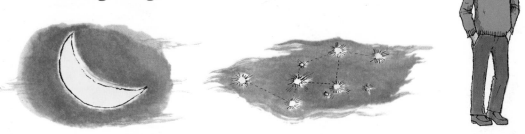

2. Can you go to the park with me?

   We are going in a **car.**

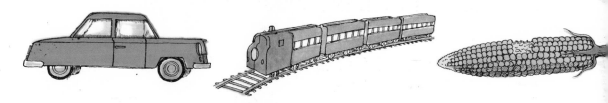

3. It's a funny, funny play.

   Come to see it and you will **smile.**

I Can't Smile

 I can't go to school today.

Mr. Day is going to take pictures.

And I can't smile.

Come here and look.

Jan, you have a nice smile.

The picture will not look nice.
I have no teeth.

Jan, you look nice.
You have to go to school.
There's Sally.

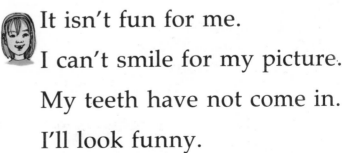

Today is picture day, Jan.
We are going to have fun.

It isn't fun for me.
I can't smile for my picture.
My teeth have not come in.
I'll look funny.

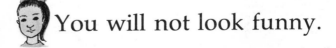

You will not look funny.

 I'll see you at the bus stop, Sally.
I have to go in here.

 I'll come in with you.

 No, you go on.

Jan's Funny Smile

 Mr. Day can take my picture now.

I'll look nice for the picture.

I can smile!

 Mr. Day is here, Jan.

He's going to take the pictures now.

Look at me and smile!
This will be a nice picture, Sally.

Will Jan's picture be nice, Mr. Day?
Jan can't smile today.

I can smile now, Sally.
I'll look nice for the picture.

Look at me, Jan. Smile!

This is going to be a funny picture.

I want a nice picture.

Take the funny teeth out, Jan.

Now we'll have a nice picture.

23

 Your pictures are here.

You can take the pictures home now.

I want to see your picture, Jan.

Where is it?

Here it is.

24

 Jan, you look funny in this picture.

I look nice, Sally.

The teeth look funny.

 Here I am without the funny teeth.

 You look nice without teeth, Jan.

 This is a nice picture.
I have a nice smile in it.

1. Will you help me, Jan?

   I want to play.

   I'm looking for my **doll.**

  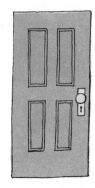

2. You can have fun playing with this.

   You go to look into it.

   And out comes a **surprise.**

 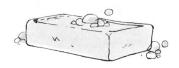 

3. He will look at your teeth.

   He can help you have nice teeth.

   He is a **dentist.**

 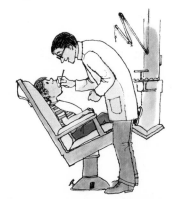 

Surprise Day at School

Jan, what is in there?

It's a surprise.

I'm going to take it to school.

Today is surprise day at school.

 What is your surprise?

 It's a frog.

 Is it a real frog?

Can you take a real frog to school?

 Today I can.

I can take a frog on surprise day.

Here is my surprise.

I want to see what you have, Jan.

 It's a surprise.

You can't look at a surprise, Sally.

 Here comes the bus.

We are going to have fun today.

What's in your box, Jan?

Do you have a tiger in there?

No, it's not a tiger.

It's my surprise.

What do you have in your box, Jan?

You can't look at it now.

It's my surprise.

You'll see it at school.

 Croak! Croak!

What's the funny noise?

What noise?

It's not me.

It's the bus.

It's a funny noise for a bus!

34

Here we are.

You'll have fun at school today.

You'll have fun with your surprises.

Can I see what's in your box, Jan?

You can't see it now, Mr. Wills.

You can see it after school.

A Surprise for Jan

Today is surprise day!

This is where your surprises go.

Now we have work to do.

We'll see the surprises after we work.

Croak! Croak!

There's the funny noise.
What can it be, Jan?

What noise?
It's not me.
It's a truck out there.
Do your work, Sally.

37

Croak! Croak!

What is the funny noise?

It's a truck out there.

No, it isn't out there.
The funny noise is in here.
It's in this box.

Jan! Look at your surprise!
Where is it going?

Help me stop it, Bob!
Go after it!

What's in your surprise box, Jan?
Look at it jump.

39

 It's a frog.
And frogs jump!
It wants to get out of the box.

 The frog is out of the box, Jan.
I'll get it for you.

Oh, Jan!
What a funny surprise!

The frog isn't a funny surprise.
The jumping box is the surprise!

41

1. We will go home on a  .

    pale   pane   plane

2. Jim wants to play with my  .

    train   turn   tailor

3. This is my box of .

    candy   crayons   carrots

4. Where do you see the  ?

    smoke   some   soak

5. This picture is in a nice .

    farm   fame   frame

6. Look at the picture on this .

    sample   stamp   sack .

Fun With a Lion

Come with me, Bob.

I'm going to the jungle.

I'm going to hunt a lion.

Where is this jungle?

Come on.

I'll take you there.

44

I'm not going to hunt for a real lion.

Real lions scare me.

 It's not a real lion.

You'll see.

There's the jungle, Bob.

Do you see that lion?

That's the lion we'll hunt.

Public Library

This isn't a real jungle.

And that lion can't run.

We can't hunt lions here.

We can play that it's a real jungle.

We can play that the lion can run.

We'll run after it.

Lion, we're going to get you!

Oh, oh! Here comes a dog!

Look at its big teeth.

This lion is scared of big dogs.

Run, Lion, run!

That big dog is after you!

47

Run, Lion, run!
You have to get away!
That big dog will get you!

What's going on out here?

A big dog is after the lion.

48

That is a nice dog.

A lion isn't scared of dogs, is it?

That lion is scared!

We have books here.

We can look at pictures of lions.

We can look at pictures of dogs.

You'll see that dogs do not scare lions.

Here are the picture books.

Look at this big dog, Jim.

Look at its big teeth.

Here is a big lion.

Look at its big teeth!

No dog can scare this lion!

 Can we take the books to school?

 You can't take a book now.

You do not have a card.

Take this home with you.

Here are your cards.

Now you can take the books to school.

Do you want to hunt in the jungle?

I'm not going to hunt now.

I want to look at this dog book.

After that I'll go hunting.

The lion will be here.

1. We are going to have a **race.**

   We will race to get that box.

   What are Jim and Bob going to do?

   > Run for a box

   > Hide in a box

2. Your play truck will not work.

   Bob will **fix** it for you.

   What will Bob do with the truck?

   > Run with it

   > Work on it

3. Look at the big tiger teeth.

   The **face** you have on scares me, Jim.

   What is Jim doing?

   > Looking at a tiger

   > Playing that he's a tiger

The Lion Gets Away

Do you want to hunt in the jungle?
We can go there on the way home.

That will be fun.
I can take this book to the library.

And I have my library card.
I can take a book out today!

The lion isn't here!

Where did it go?

How did it get away?

It's not a real lion.

The lion isn't out there.

How did it get away?

The lion will not be at the library.

Where will it be?

That will be a surprise for you.

The lion is on a truck now.

Have you seen a lion on a truck?

No, I have not seen one on a truck.
I've seen one at the zoo.

The lion we're looking for isn't real.
It's a play lion.

How can we find it?

I've seen lions in there.
You can go in there and hunt for it.

59

Not That Lion!

We are looking for a lion.
Do you have one in here?

I'll take you to see the lion.
It's in here.

60

 That's a real lion!

That's not the one we are hunting for.

We want to find the library lion.

 It's on a truck.

We can't find the truck.

And we can't find the lion.

Will you help?

I'll find out where the lion's going.

I have a nice surprise for you!
The library lion is in the park.

I can't see a truck.

And I can't see the lion.

It's not here, Jim!

There it is, Bob!

There's the library lion!

And there's that big dog!

63

That dog is not big.

Lions are not scared of dogs.

And I'm not scared.

Come on!

This lion hunt is going to be fun!

FOR THE
CHILDREN OF
RIVERDALE

64